Created and published by Knock Knock
Distributed by Who's There Inc.
Venice, CA 90291
knockknockstuff.com

ISBN: 978-160106627-5
UPC: 825703-50033-2

20 19 18 17 16 15 14 13 12 11 10 9 8 7 6 5 4 3 2 1

COUCH

Guest Book

KNOCK KNOCK®
VENICE, CALIFORNIA

Memorable Moments: _____

_____

_____

_____

_____

_____

Additional Sentiments: _____

_____

_____

_____

_____

_____

Welcome to My Couch

DATE OF VISIT: ....

TIME OF VISIT: .... AM / PM

NAME OF CANDY THAT BEST DESCRIBES THE PEOPLE ON THIS COUCH:

☐ Smarties
☐ Dum-Dums
☐ SweeTARTS
☐ Peeps
☐ Goobers
☐ Hot Tamales
☐ Nerds

COUCH POTATO SPECTRUM

Shade in the potato to represent where you fall on the couch-potato spectrum.

TOTALLY CHARMING GUEST
TOTAL COUCH POTATO

SIGN IN, PLEASE

ACTIVITIES PERFORMED ON THIS COUCH:

☐ Watching TV   ☐ Chatting   ☐ Chilling out
☐ Playing games ☐ Sleeping   ☐ Making out
☐ Thinking   ☐ Surfing   ☐ ....

OTHERS IN ATTENDANCE:

....

COUCH THOUGHTS

LENGTH OF TIME SPENT ON COUCH:

.... Days   .... Hours   .... Minutes

SEARCH CUSHIONS FOR CHANGE?

☐ Yes, of course   ☐ No, of course not

DID YOU RETURN IT?

☐ Yes, of course   ☐ No, of course not

AMOUNT FOUND: $............................

OTHER ITEMS FOUND IN CUSHIONS:

....
....

REPORT CARD	A	B	C	D	F
Ambience					
Comfort					
Cleanliness					
Refreshments					
Roominess					
Conviviality					
OVERALL					

Memorable Moments: _____

_____

_____

_____

_____

Additional Sentiments: _____

_____

_____

_____

_____

Welcome to My Couch

DATE OF VISIT: ....

TIME OF VISIT: .... AM / PM

NAME OF CANDY THAT BEST DESCRIBES THE PEOPLE ON THIS COUCH:

- ☐ Smarties
- ☐ Dum-Dums
- ☐ SweeTARTS
- ☐ Peeps
- ☐ Goobers
- ☐ Hot Tamales
- ☐ Nerds

COUCH POTATO SPECTRUM

Shade in the potato to represent where you fall on the couch-potato spectrum.

TOTALLY CHARMING GUEST   TOTAL COUCH POTATO

SIGN IN, PLEASE

ACTIVITIES PERFORMED ON THIS COUCH:

☐ Watching TV	☐ Chatting	☐ Chilling out
☐ Playing games	☐ Sleeping	☐ Making out
☐ Thinking	☐ Surfing	☐ ....

OTHERS IN ATTENDANCE:

....

COUCH THOUGHTS

LENGTH OF TIME SPENT ON COUCH:

.... Days .... Hours .... Minutes

SEARCH CUSHIONS FOR CHANGE?

☐ Yes, of course   ☐ No, of course not

DID YOU RETURN IT?

☐ Yes, of course   ☐ No, of course not

AMOUNT FOUND: $..............................

OTHER ITEMS FOUND IN CUSHIONS:

....

....

REPORT CARD	A	B	C	D	F
Ambience					
Comfort					
Cleanliness					
Refreshments					
Roominess					
Conviviality					
OVERALL					

Memorable Moments: _____

_____

_____

_____

_____

_____

Additional Sentiments: _____

_____

_____

_____

_____

_____

Welcome to My Couch

DATE OF VISIT: ....

TIME OF VISIT: .... AM / PM

NAME OF CANDY THAT BEST DESCRIBES THE PEOPLE ON THIS COUCH:

☐ Smarties
☐ Dum-Dums
☐ SweeTARTS
☐ Peeps
☐ Goobers
☐ Hot Tamales
☐ Nerds

COUCH POTATO SPECTRUM

Shade in the potato to represent where you fall on the couch-potato spectrum.

TOTALLY CHARMING GUEST

TOTAL COUCH POTATO

SIGN IN, PLEASE

ACTIVITIES PERFORMED ON THIS COUCH:

☐ Watching TV   ☐ Chatting   ☐ Chilling out
☐ Playing games   ☐ Sleeping   ☐ Making out
☐ Thinking   ☐ Surfing   ☐ ....

OTHERS IN ATTENDANCE:

....

COUCH THOUGHTS

LENGTH OF TIME SPENT ON COUCH:

.... Days   .... Hours   .... Minutes

SEARCH CUSHIONS FOR CHANGE?

☐ Yes, of course   ☐ No, of course not

DID YOU RETURN IT?

☐ Yes, of course   ☐ No, of course not

AMOUNT FOUND: $...........................

OTHER ITEMS FOUND IN CUSHIONS:

....
....

REPORT CARD	A	B	C	D	F
Ambience					
Comfort					
Cleanliness					
Refreshments					
Roominess					
Conviviality					
OVERALL					

Memorable Moments: _____

_____

_____

_____

_____

_____

Additional Sentiments: _____

_____

_____

_____

_____

_____

Welcome to My Couch

DATE OF VISIT: ....

TIME OF VISIT: .... AM / PM

NAME OF CANDY THAT BEST DESCRIBES THE PEOPLE ON THIS COUCH:

- ☐ Smarties
- ☐ Dum-Dums
- ☐ SweeTARTS
- ☐ Peeps
- ☐ Goobers
- ☐ Hot Tamales
- ☐ Nerds

COUCH POTATO SPECTRUM

Shade in the potato to represent where you fall on the couch-potato spectrum.

TOTALLY CHARMING GUEST — TOTAL COUCH POTATO

SIGN IN, PLEASE

ACTIVITIES PERFORMED ON THIS COUCH:

- ☐ Watching TV
- ☐ Playing games
- ☐ Thinking
- ☐ Chatting
- ☐ Sleeping
- ☐ Surfing
- ☐ Chilling out
- ☐ Making out
- ☐ ....

OTHERS IN ATTENDANCE:

....

COUCH THOUGHTS

LENGTH OF TIME SPENT ON COUCH:

.... Days   .... Hours   .... Minutes

SEARCH CUSHIONS FOR CHANGE?

☐ Yes, of course   ☐ No, of course not

DID YOU RETURN IT?

☐ Yes, of course   ☐ No, of course not

AMOUNT FOUND: $.............................

OTHER ITEMS FOUND IN CUSHIONS:

....

....

REPORT CARD	A	B	C	D	F
Ambience					
Comfort					
Cleanliness					
Refreshments					
Roominess					
Conviviality					
OVERALL					

Memorable Moments: _____
_____
_____
_____
_____
_____

Additional Sentiments: _____
_____
_____
_____
_____
_____

Welcome to My Couch

DATE OF VISIT: ....

TIME OF VISIT: .... AM / PM

NAME OF CANDY THAT BEST DESCRIBES THE PEOPLE ON THIS COUCH:

- ☐ Smarties
- ☐ Dum-Dums
- ☐ SweeTARTS
- ☐ Peeps
- ☐ Goobers
- ☐ Hot Tamales
- ☐ Nerds

COUCH POTATO SPECTRUM

Shade in the potato to represent where you fall on the couch-potato spectrum.

TOTALLY CHARMING GUEST — TOTAL COUCH POTATO

SIGN IN, PLEASE

ACTIVITIES PERFORMED ON THIS COUCH:

- ☐ Watching TV
- ☐ Playing games
- ☐ Thinking
- ☐ Chatting
- ☐ Sleeping
- ☐ Surfing
- ☐ Chilling out
- ☐ Making out
- ☐ ....

OTHERS IN ATTENDANCE:

....

COUCH THOUGHTS

LENGTH OF TIME SPENT ON COUCH:

...... Days .... Hours .... Minutes

SEARCH CUSHIONS FOR CHANGE?

☐ Yes, of course   ☐ No, of course not

DID YOU RETURN IT?

☐ Yes, of course   ☐ No, of course not

AMOUNT FOUND: $............................

OTHER ITEMS FOUND IN CUSHIONS:

....

....

REPORT CARD	A	B	C	D	F
Ambience					
Comfort					
Cleanliness					
Refreshments					
Roominess					
Conviviality					
OVERALL					

Memorable Moments: _____

_____

_____

_____

_____

_____

Additional Sentiments: _____

_____

_____

_____

_____

_____

Welcome to My Couch

DATE OF VISIT: ....

TIME OF VISIT: .... AM / PM

NAME OF CANDY THAT BEST DESCRIBES THE PEOPLE ON THIS COUCH:

- ☐ Smarties
- ☐ Dum-Dums
- ☐ SweeTARTS
- ☐ Peeps
- ☐ Goobers
- ☐ Hot Tamales
- ☐ Nerds

COUCH POTATO SPECTRUM

Shade in the potato to represent where you fall on the couch-potato spectrum.

TOTALLY
CHARMING
GUEST

TOTAL
COUCH
POTATO

SIGN IN, PLEASE

ACTIVITIES PERFORMED ON THIS COUCH:

- ☐ Watching TV
- ☐ Playing games
- ☐ Thinking
- ☐ Chatting
- ☐ Sleeping
- ☐ Surfing
- ☐ Chilling out
- ☐ Making out
- ☐ ....

OTHERS IN ATTENDANCE:

....

COUCH THOUGHTS

LENGTH OF TIME SPENT ON COUCH:

...... Days .... Hours .... Minutes

SEARCH CUSHIONS FOR CHANGE?

☐ Yes, of course   ☐ No, of course not

DID YOU RETURN IT?

☐ Yes, of course   ☐ No, of course not

AMOUNT FOUND: $............................

OTHER ITEMS FOUND IN CUSHIONS:

....
....
....

REPORT CARD	A	B	C	D	F
Ambience					
Comfort					
Cleanliness					
Refreshments					
Roominess					
Conviviality					
OVERALL					

Memorable Moments: _____

_____

_____

_____

_____

_____

Additional Sentiments: _____

_____

_____

_____

_____

_____

Welcome to My Couch

DATE OF VISIT: ....

TIME OF VISIT: .... AM / PM

NAME OF CANDY THAT BEST DESCRIBES THE PEOPLE ON THIS COUCH:

- ☐ Smarties
- ☐ Dum-Dums
- ☐ SweeTARTS
- ☐ Peeps
- ☐ Goobers
- ☐ Hot Tamales
- ☐ Nerds

COUCH POTATO SPECTRUM

Shade in the potato to represent where you fall on the couch-potato spectrum.

TOTALLY CHARMING GUEST   TOTAL COUCH POTATO

SIGN IN, PLEASE

ACTIVITIES PERFORMED ON THIS COUCH:

- ☐ Watching TV
- ☐ Playing games
- ☐ Thinking
- ☐ Chatting
- ☐ Sleeping
- ☐ Surfing
- ☐ Chilling out
- ☐ Making out
- ☐ ....

OTHERS IN ATTENDANCE:

....

COUCH THOUGHTS

LENGTH OF TIME SPENT ON COUCH:

...... Days   .... Hours   .... Minutes

SEARCH CUSHIONS FOR CHANGE?

☐ Yes, of course   ☐ No, of course not

DID YOU RETURN IT?

☐ Yes, of course   ☐ No, of course not

AMOUNT FOUND: $............................

OTHER ITEMS FOUND IN CUSHIONS:

....

....

REPORT CARD	A	B	C	D	F
Ambience					
Comfort					
Cleanliness					
Refreshments					
Roominess					
Conviviality					
OVERALL					

Memorable Moments: _____
_____
_____
_____
_____
_____

Additional Sentiments: _____
_____
_____
_____
_____
_____

Welcome to My Couch

DATE OF VISIT: ....

TIME OF VISIT: .... AM / PM

NAME OF CANDY THAT BEST DESCRIBES THE PEOPLE ON THIS COUCH:

- ☐ Smarties
- ☐ Dum-Dums
- ☐ SweeTARTS
- ☐ Peeps
- ☐ Goobers
- ☐ Hot Tamales
- ☐ Nerds

COUCH POTATO SPECTRUM

Shade in the potato to represent where you fall on the couch-potato spectrum.

TOTALLY CHARMING GUEST

TOTAL COUCH POTATO

SIGN IN, PLEASE

ACTIVITIES PERFORMED ON THIS COUCH:

- ☐ Watching TV
- ☐ Playing games
- ☐ Thinking
- ☐ Chatting
- ☐ Sleeping
- ☐ Surfing
- ☐ Chilling out
- ☐ Making out
- ☐ ....

OTHERS IN ATTENDANCE:

....

COUCH THOUGHTS

LENGTH OF TIME SPENT ON COUCH:

...... Days .... Hours .... Minutes

SEARCH CUSHIONS FOR CHANGE?

☐ Yes, of course   ☐ No, of course not

DID YOU RETURN IT?

☐ Yes, of course   ☐ No, of course not

AMOUNT FOUND: $...........................

OTHER ITEMS FOUND IN CUSHIONS:

....

....

REPORT CARD	A	B	C	D	F
Ambience					
Comfort					
Cleanliness					
Refreshments					
Roominess					
Conviviality					
OVERALL					

Memorable Moments: _____

_____

_____

_____

_____

_____

Additional Sentiments: _____

_____

_____

_____

_____

_____

Welcome to My Couch

DATE OF VISIT: ....

TIME OF VISIT: .... AM / PM

NAME OF CANDY THAT BEST DESCRIBES THE PEOPLE ON THIS COUCH:

- ☐ Smarties
- ☐ Dum-Dums
- ☐ SweeTARTS
- ☐ Peeps
- ☐ Goobers
- ☐ Hot Tamales
- ☐ Nerds

COUCH POTATO SPECTRUM

Shade in the potato to represent where you fall on the couch-potato spectrum.

TOTALLY CHARMING GUEST — TOTAL COUCH POTATO

SIGN IN, PLEASE

ACTIVITIES PERFORMED ON THIS COUCH:

- ☐ Watching TV
- ☐ Playing games
- ☐ Thinking
- ☐ Chatting
- ☐ Sleeping
- ☐ Surfing
- ☐ Chilling out
- ☐ Making out
- ☐ ....

OTHERS IN ATTENDANCE:

....

COUCH THOUGHTS

LENGTH OF TIME SPENT ON COUCH:

.... Days   .... Hours   .... Minutes

SEARCH CUSHIONS FOR CHANGE?
☐ Yes, of course   ☐ No, of course not

DID YOU RETURN IT?
☐ Yes, of course   ☐ No, of course not

AMOUNT FOUND: $............................

OTHER ITEMS FOUND IN CUSHIONS:

....

....

REPORT CARD	A	B	C	D	F
Ambience					
Comfort					
Cleanliness					
Refreshments					
Roominess					
Conviviality					
OVERALL					

Memorable Moments: _____

_____

_____

_____

_____

_____

Additional Sentiments: _____

_____

_____

_____

_____

_____

Welcome to My Couch

DATE OF VISIT: ....

TIME OF VISIT: .... AM / PM

NAME OF CANDY THAT BEST DESCRIBES THE PEOPLE ON THIS COUCH:

- ☐ Smarties
- ☐ Dum-Dums
- ☐ SweeTARTS
- ☐ Peeps
- ☐ Goobers
- ☐ Hot Tamales
- ☐ Nerds

COUCH POTATO SPECTRUM

Shade in the potato to represent where you fall on the couch-potato spectrum.

TOTALLY
CHARMING
GUEST

TOTAL
COUCH
POTATO

SIGN IN, PLEASE

ACTIVITIES PERFORMED ON THIS COUCH:

- ☐ Watching TV
- ☐ Playing games
- ☐ Thinking
- ☐ Chatting
- ☐ Sleeping
- ☐ Surfing
- ☐ Chilling out
- ☐ Making out
- ☐ ....

OTHERS IN ATTENDANCE:

....

COUCH THOUGHTS

LENGTH OF TIME SPENT ON COUCH:

.... Days .... Hours .... Minutes

SEARCH CUSHIONS FOR CHANGE?

☐ Yes, of course ☐ No, of course not

DID YOU RETURN IT?

☐ Yes, of course ☐ No, of course not

AMOUNT FOUND: $............................

OTHER ITEMS FOUND IN CUSHIONS:

....

....

REPORT CARD	A	B	C	D	F
Ambience					
Comfort					
Cleanliness					
Refreshments					
Roominess					
Conviviality					
OVERALL					

Memorable Moments: _____

_____

_____

_____

_____

_____

Additional Sentiments: _____

_____

_____

_____

_____

_____

Welcome to My Couch

DATE OF VISIT: ....

TIME OF VISIT: .... AM / PM

NAME OF CANDY THAT BEST DESCRIBES THE PEOPLE ON THIS COUCH:

- ☐ Smarties
- ☐ Dum-Dums
- ☐ SweeTARTS
- ☐ Peeps
- ☐ Goobers
- ☐ Hot Tamales
- ☐ Nerds

COUCH POTATO SPECTRUM

Shade in the potato to represent where you fall on the couch-potato spectrum.

TOTALLY CHARMING GUEST .... TOTAL COUCH POTATO

SIGN IN, PLEASE

ACTIVITIES PERFORMED ON THIS COUCH:

- ☐ Watching TV
- ☐ Playing games
- ☐ Thinking
- ☐ Chatting
- ☐ Sleeping
- ☐ Surfing
- ☐ Chilling out
- ☐ Making out
- ☐ ....

OTHERS IN ATTENDANCE:

....

COUCH THOUGHTS

LENGTH OF TIME SPENT ON COUCH:

.... Days   .... Hours   .... Minutes

SEARCH CUSHIONS FOR CHANGE?

☐ Yes, of course   ☐ No, of course not

DID YOU RETURN IT?

☐ Yes, of course   ☐ No, of course not

AMOUNT FOUND: $..........................

OTHER ITEMS FOUND IN CUSHIONS:

....
....

REPORT CARD	A	B	C	D	F
Ambience					
Comfort					
Cleanliness					
Refreshments					
Roominess					
Conviviality					
OVERALL					

Memorable Moments: _____

_____

_____

_____

_____

_____

Additional Sentiments: _____

_____

_____

_____

_____

_____

Welcome to My Couch

DATE OF VISIT: ....

TIME OF VISIT: .... AM / PM

NAME OF CANDY THAT BEST DESCRIBES THE PEOPLE ON THIS COUCH:

- ☐ Smarties
- ☐ Dum-Dums
- ☐ SweeTARTS
- ☐ Peeps
- ☐ Goobers
- ☐ Hot Tamales
- ☐ Nerds

COUCH POTATO SPECTRUM

Shade in the potato to represent where you fall on the couch-potato spectrum.

TOTALLY CHARMING GUEST   TOTAL COUCH POTATO

SIGN IN, PLEASE

ACTIVITIES PERFORMED ON THIS COUCH:

- ☐ Watching TV
- ☐ Playing games
- ☐ Thinking
- ☐ Chatting
- ☐ Sleeping
- ☐ Surfing
- ☐ Chilling out
- ☐ Making out
- ☐ ....

OTHERS IN ATTENDANCE:

....

COUCH THOUGHTS

LENGTH OF TIME SPENT ON COUCH:

...... Days .... Hours .... Minutes

SEARCH CUSHIONS FOR CHANGE?

☐ Yes, of course ☐ No, of course not

DID YOU RETURN IT?

☐ Yes, of course ☐ No, of course not

AMOUNT FOUND: $............................

OTHER ITEMS FOUND IN CUSHIONS:

....

....

REPORT CARD	A	B	C	D	F
Ambience					
Comfort					
Cleanliness					
Refreshments					
Roominess					
Conviviality					
OVERALL					

Memorable Moments: _____

_____

_____

_____

_____

_____

Additional Sentiments: _____

_____

_____

_____

_____

_____

Welcome to My Couch

DATE OF VISIT: ....

TIME OF VISIT: .... AM / PM

NAME OF CANDY THAT BEST DESCRIBES THE PEOPLE ON THIS COUCH:

- ☐ Smarties
- ☐ Dum-Dums
- ☐ SweeTARTS
- ☐ Peeps
- ☐ Goobers
- ☐ Hot Tamales
- ☐ Nerds

COUCH POTATO SPECTRUM

Shade in the potato to represent where you fall on the couch-potato spectrum.

TOTALLY CHARMING GUEST — TOTAL COUCH POTATO

SIGN IN, PLEASE

ACTIVITIES PERFORMED ON THIS COUCH:

- ☐ Watching TV
- ☐ Chatting
- ☐ Chilling out
- ☐ Playing games
- ☐ Sleeping
- ☐ Making out
- ☐ Thinking
- ☐ Surfing
- ☐ ....

OTHERS IN ATTENDANCE:

....

COUCH THOUGHTS

LENGTH OF TIME SPENT ON COUCH:

...... Days .... Hours .... Minutes

SEARCH CUSHIONS FOR CHANGE?

☐ Yes, of course   ☐ No, of course not

DID YOU RETURN IT?

☐ Yes, of course   ☐ No, of course not

AMOUNT FOUND: $.............................

OTHER ITEMS FOUND IN CUSHIONS:

....
....

REPORT CARD	A	B	C	D	F
Ambience					
Comfort					
Cleanliness					
Refreshments					
Roominess					
Conviviality					
OVERALL					

Memorable Moments: _____

_____

_____

_____

_____

_____

Additional Sentiments: _____

_____

_____

_____

_____

_____

Welcome to My Couch

DATE OF VISIT: ....

TIME OF VISIT: .... AM / PM

NAME OF CANDY THAT BEST DESCRIBES THE PEOPLE ON THIS COUCH:

- ☐ Smarties
- ☐ Dum-Dums
- ☐ SweeTARTS
- ☐ Peeps
- ☐ Goobers
- ☐ Hot Tamales
- ☐ Nerds

COUCH POTATO SPECTRUM
Shade in the potato to represent where you fall on the couch-potato spectrum.

TOTALLY
CHARMING
GUEST

TOTAL
COUCH
POTATO

SIGN IN, PLEASE

ACTIVITIES PERFORMED ON THIS COUCH:

- ☐ Watching TV
- ☐ Playing games
- ☐ Thinking
- ☐ Chatting
- ☐ Sleeping
- ☐ Surfing
- ☐ Chilling out
- ☐ Making out
- ☐ ....

OTHERS IN ATTENDANCE:
....

COUCH THOUGHTS

LENGTH OF TIME SPENT ON COUCH:
.... Days   .... Hours   .... Minutes

SEARCH CUSHIONS FOR CHANGE?
☐ Yes, of course   ☐ No, of course not

DID YOU RETURN IT?
☐ Yes, of course   ☐ No, of course not

AMOUNT FOUND: $............................

OTHER ITEMS FOUND IN CUSHIONS:
....
....

REPORT CARD	A	B	C	D	F
Ambience					
Comfort					
Cleanliness					
Refreshments					
Roominess					
Conviviality					
OVERALL					

Memorable Moments: _____

_____

_____

_____

_____

_____

Additional Sentiments: _____

_____

_____

_____

_____

_____

Welcome to My Couch

DATE OF VISIT: ....

TIME OF VISIT: .... AM / PM

NAME OF CANDY THAT BEST DESCRIBES THE PEOPLE ON THIS COUCH:

- ☐ Smarties
- ☐ Dum-Dums
- ☐ SweeTARTS
- ☐ Peeps
- ☐ Goobers
- ☐ Hot Tamales
- ☐ Nerds

COUCH POTATO SPECTRUM
Shade in the potato to represent where you fall on the couch-potato spectrum.

TOTALLY CHARMING GUEST

TOTAL COUCH POTATO

SIGN IN, PLEASE

ACTIVITIES PERFORMED ON THIS COUCH:

- ☐ Watching TV
- ☐ Playing games
- ☐ Thinking
- ☐ Chatting
- ☐ Sleeping
- ☐ Surfing
- ☐ Chilling out
- ☐ Making out
- ☐ ....

OTHERS IN ATTENDANCE:

....

COUCH THOUGHTS

LENGTH OF TIME SPENT ON COUCH:

.... Days   .... Hours   .... Minutes

SEARCH CUSHIONS FOR CHANGE?

☐ Yes, of course   ☐ No, of course not

DID YOU RETURN IT?

☐ Yes, of course   ☐ No, of course not

AMOUNT FOUND: $.............................

OTHER ITEMS FOUND IN CUSHIONS:

....

....

REPORT CARD	A	B	C	D	F
Ambience					
Comfort					
Cleanliness					
Refreshments					
Roominess					
Conviviality					
OVERALL					

Memorable Moments: _____
_____
_____
_____
_____
_____

Additional Sentiments: _____
_____
_____
_____
_____
_____

Welcome to My Couch

DATE OF VISIT: ....

TIME OF VISIT: .... AM / PM

NAME OF CANDY THAT BEST DESCRIBES THE PEOPLE ON THIS COUCH:

☐ Smarties
☐ Dum-Dums
☐ SweeTARTS
☐ Peeps
☐ Goobers
☐ Hot Tamales
☐ Nerds

COUCH POTATO SPECTRUM

Shade in the potato to represent where you fall on the couch-potato spectrum.

TOTALLY CHARMING GUEST

TOTAL COUCH POTATO

SIGN IN, PLEASE

ACTIVITIES PERFORMED ON THIS COUCH:

☐ Watching TV   ☐ Chatting   ☐ Chilling out
☐ Playing games   ☐ Sleeping   ☐ Making out
☐ Thinking   ☐ Surfing   ☐ ....

OTHERS IN ATTENDANCE:

....

COUCH THOUGHTS

LENGTH OF TIME SPENT ON COUCH:

...... Days .... Hours .... Minutes

SEARCH CUSHIONS FOR CHANGE?

☐ Yes, of course   ☐ No, of course not

DID YOU RETURN IT?

☐ Yes, of course   ☐ No, of course not

AMOUNT FOUND: $..............................

OTHER ITEMS FOUND IN CUSHIONS:

....

....

REPORT CARD	A	B	C	D	F
Ambience					
Comfort					
Cleanliness					
Refreshments					
Roominess					
Conviviality					
OVERALL					

Memorable Moments: _____

_____

_____

_____

_____

_____

Additional Sentiments: _____

_____

_____

_____

_____

_____

Welcome to My Couch

DATE OF VISIT: ....

TIME OF VISIT: .... AM / PM

NAME OF CANDY THAT BEST DESCRIBES THE PEOPLE ON THIS COUCH:

☐ Smarties
☐ Dum-Dums
☐ SweeTARTS
☐ Peeps
☐ Goobers
☐ Hot Tamales
☐ Nerds

COUCH POTATO SPECTRUM
Shade in the potato to represent where you fall on the couch-potato spectrum.

TOTALLY
CHARMING
GUEST

TOTAL
COUCH
POTATO

SIGN IN, PLEASE

ACTIVITIES PERFORMED ON THIS COUCH:

☐ Watching TV   ☐ Chatting   ☐ Chilling out
☐ Playing games   ☐ Sleeping   ☐ Making out
☐ Thinking   ☐ Surfing   ☐ ....

OTHERS IN ATTENDANCE:

....

COUCH THOUGHTS

LENGTH OF TIME SPENT ON COUCH:

...... Days .... Hours .... Minutes

SEARCH CUSHIONS FOR CHANGE?
☐ Yes, of course ☐ No, of course not

DID YOU RETURN IT?
☐ Yes, of course ☐ No, of course not

AMOUNT FOUND: $...........................

OTHER ITEMS FOUND IN CUSHIONS:

....
....

REPORT CARD	A	B	C	D	F
Ambience					
Comfort					
Cleanliness					
Refreshments					
Roominess					
Conviviality					
OVERALL					

Memorable Moments: _____

_____

_____

_____

_____

_____

Additional Sentiments: _____

_____

_____

_____

_____

_____

Welcome to My Couch

DATE OF VISIT: ....

TIME OF VISIT: .... AM / PM

SIGN IN, PLEASE

LENGTH OF TIME SPENT ON COUCH:

.... Days   .... Hours   .... Minutes

NAME OF CANDY THAT BEST DESCRIBES THE PEOPLE ON THIS COUCH:

☐ Smarties
☐ Dum-Dums
☐ SweeTARTS
☐ Peeps
☐ Goobers
☐ Hot Tamales
☐ Nerds

ACTIVITIES PERFORMED ON THIS COUCH:

☐ Watching TV   ☐ Chatting   ☐ Chilling out
☐ Playing games   ☐ Sleeping   ☐ Making out
☐ Thinking   ☐ Surfing   ☐ ....

OTHERS IN ATTENDANCE:

....

COUCH THOUGHTS

SEARCH CUSHIONS FOR CHANGE?

☐ Yes, of course   ☐ No, of course not

DID YOU RETURN IT?

☐ Yes, of course   ☐ No, of course not

AMOUNT FOUND: $.............................

OTHER ITEMS FOUND IN CUSHIONS:

....

....

COUCH POTATO SPECTRUM

Shade in the potato to represent where you fall on the couch-potato spectrum.

TOTALLY CHARMING GUEST   TOTAL COUCH POTATO

REPORT CARD	A	B	C	D	F
Ambience					
Comfort					
Cleanliness					
Refreshments					
Roominess					
Conviviality					
OVERALL					

Memorable Moments: _____

_____

_____

_____

_____

_____

Additional Sentiments: _____

_____

_____

_____

_____

_____

Welcome to My Couch

DATE OF VISIT: ....

TIME OF VISIT: .... AM / PM

SIGN IN, PLEASE

LENGTH OF TIME SPENT ON COUCH:

.... Days   .... Hours   .... Minutes

NAME OF CANDY THAT BEST DESCRIBES THE PEOPLE ON THIS COUCH:

- ☐ Smarties
- ☐ Dum-Dums
- ☐ SweeTARTS
- ☐ Peeps
- ☐ Goobers
- ☐ Hot Tamales
- ☐ Nerds

ACTIVITIES PERFORMED ON THIS COUCH:

- ☐ Watching TV
- ☐ Playing games
- ☐ Thinking
- ☐ Chatting
- ☐ Sleeping
- ☐ Surfing
- ☐ Chilling out
- ☐ Making out
- ☐ ....

OTHERS IN ATTENDANCE:

....

COUCH THOUGHTS

SEARCH CUSHIONS FOR CHANGE?

☐ Yes, of course   ☐ No, of course not

DID YOU RETURN IT?

☐ Yes, of course   ☐ No, of course not

AMOUNT FOUND: $............................

OTHER ITEMS FOUND IN CUSHIONS:

....

....

....

COUCH POTATO SPECTRUM

Shade in the potato to represent where you fall on the couch-potato spectrum.

TOTALLY CHARMING GUEST

TOTAL COUCH POTATO

REPORT CARD	A	B	C	D	F
Ambience					
Comfort					
Cleanliness					
Refreshments					
Roominess					
Conviviality					
OVERALL					

Memorable Moments: _____

_____

_____

_____

_____

_____

Additional Sentiments: _____

_____

_____

_____

_____

_____

Welcome to My Couch

DATE OF VISIT: ....

TIME OF VISIT: .... AM / PM

NAME OF CANDY THAT BEST DESCRIBES THE PEOPLE ON THIS COUCH:

- ☐ Smarties
- ☐ Dum-Dums
- ☐ SweeTARTS
- ☐ Peeps
- ☐ Goobers
- ☐ Hot Tamales
- ☐ Nerds

COUCH POTATO SPECTRUM

Shade in the potato to represent where you fall on the couch-potato spectrum.

TOTALLY CHARMING GUEST — TOTAL COUCH POTATO

SIGN IN, PLEASE

ACTIVITIES PERFORMED ON THIS COUCH:

- ☐ Watching TV
- ☐ Playing games
- ☐ Thinking
- ☐ Chatting
- ☐ Sleeping
- ☐ Surfing
- ☐ Chilling out
- ☐ Making out
- ☐ ....

OTHERS IN ATTENDANCE:

....

COUCH THOUGHTS

LENGTH OF TIME SPENT ON COUCH:

...... Days   .... Hours   .... Minutes

SEARCH CUSHIONS FOR CHANGE?

☐ Yes, of course   ☐ No, of course not

DID YOU RETURN IT?

☐ Yes, of course   ☐ No, of course not

AMOUNT FOUND: $............................

OTHER ITEMS FOUND IN CUSHIONS:

....

....

REPORT CARD	A	B	C	D	F
Ambience					
Comfort					
Cleanliness					
Refreshments					
Roominess					
Conviviality					
OVERALL					

Memorable Moments: _____

_____

_____

_____

_____

_____

Additional Sentiments: _____

_____

_____

_____

_____

_____

Welcome to My Couch

DATE OF VISIT: ....

TIME OF VISIT: .... AM / PM

SIGN IN, PLEASE

LENGTH OF TIME SPENT ON COUCH:

.... Days   .... Hours   .... Minutes

NAME OF CANDY THAT BEST DESCRIBES THE PEOPLE ON THIS COUCH:

☐ Smarties
☐ Dum-Dums
☐ SweeTARTS
☐ Peeps
☐ Goobers
☐ Hot Tamales
☐ Nerds

ACTIVITIES PERFORMED ON THIS COUCH:

☐ Watching TV   ☐ Chatting   ☐ Chilling out
☐ Playing games   ☐ Sleeping   ☐ Making out
☐ Thinking   ☐ Surfing   ☐ ....

OTHERS IN ATTENDANCE:

....

COUCH THOUGHTS

SEARCH CUSHIONS FOR CHANGE?
☐ Yes, of course   ☐ No, of course not

DID YOU RETURN IT?
☐ Yes, of course   ☐ No, of course not

AMOUNT FOUND: $............................

OTHER ITEMS FOUND IN CUSHIONS:
....
....

COUCH POTATO SPECTRUM

Shade in the potato to represent where you fall on the couch-potato spectrum.

TOTALLY
CHARMING
GUEST

TOTAL
COUCH
POTATO

REPORT CARD	A	B	C	D	F
Ambience					
Comfort					
Cleanliness					
Refreshments					
Roominess					
Conviviality					
OVERALL					

Memorable Moments: _____

_____

_____

_____

_____

_____

Additional Sentiments: _____

_____

_____

_____

_____

_____

Welcome to My Couch

DATE OF VISIT: ....

TIME OF VISIT: .... AM / PM

NAME OF CANDY THAT BEST DESCRIBES THE PEOPLE ON THIS COUCH:

- ☐ Smarties
- ☐ Dum-Dums
- ☐ SweeTARTS
- ☐ Peeps
- ☐ Goobers
- ☐ Hot Tamales
- ☐ Nerds

COUCH POTATO SPECTRUM
Shade in the potato to represent where you fall on the couch-potato spectrum.

TOTALLY CHARMING GUEST

TOTAL COUCH POTATO

SIGN IN, PLEASE

ACTIVITIES PERFORMED ON THIS COUCH:

- ☐ Watching TV
- ☐ Playing games
- ☐ Thinking
- ☐ Chatting
- ☐ Sleeping
- ☐ Surfing
- ☐ Chilling out
- ☐ Making out
- ☐ ....

OTHERS IN ATTENDANCE:

....

COUCH THOUGHTS

LENGTH OF TIME SPENT ON COUCH:

...... Days .... Hours .... Minutes

SEARCH CUSHIONS FOR CHANGE?
☐ Yes, of course   ☐ No, of course not

DID YOU RETURN IT?
☐ Yes, of course   ☐ No, of course not

AMOUNT FOUND: $...........................

OTHER ITEMS FOUND IN CUSHIONS:

....

....

REPORT CARD	A	B	C	D	F
Ambience					
Comfort					
Cleanliness					
Refreshments					
Roominess					
Conviviality					
OVERALL					

Memorable Moments: _____
_____
_____
_____
_____
_____

Additional Sentiments: _____
_____
_____
_____
_____
_____

Welcome to My Couch

DATE OF VISIT: ....

TIME OF VISIT: .... AM / PM

NAME OF CANDY THAT BEST DESCRIBES THE PEOPLE ON THIS COUCH:

- ☐ Smarties
- ☐ Dum-Dums
- ☐ SweeTARTS
- ☐ Peeps
- ☐ Goobers
- ☐ Hot Tamales
- ☐ Nerds

COUCH POTATO SPECTRUM

Shade in the potato to represent where you fall on the couch-potato spectrum.

TOTALLY CHARMING GUEST   TOTAL COUCH POTATO

SIGN IN, PLEASE

ACTIVITIES PERFORMED ON THIS COUCH:

- ☐ Watching TV
- ☐ Playing games
- ☐ Thinking
- ☐ Chatting
- ☐ Sleeping
- ☐ Surfing
- ☐ Chilling out
- ☐ Making out
- ☐ ....

OTHERS IN ATTENDANCE:

....

COUCH THOUGHTS

LENGTH OF TIME SPENT ON COUCH:

.... Days .... Hours .... Minutes

SEARCH CUSHIONS FOR CHANGE?

☐ Yes, of course   ☐ No, of course not

DID YOU RETURN IT?

☐ Yes, of course   ☐ No, of course not

AMOUNT FOUND: $..............................

OTHER ITEMS FOUND IN CUSHIONS:

....

....

REPORT CARD	A	B	C	D	F
Ambience					
Comfort					
Cleanliness					
Refreshments					
Roominess					
Conviviality					
OVERALL					

Memorable Moments: _____

_____

_____

_____

_____

_____

Additional Sentiments: _____

_____

_____

_____

_____

_____

Welcome to My Couch

DATE OF VISIT:	**SIGN IN, PLEASE**	**LENGTH OF TIME SPENT ON COUCH:**
TIME OF VISIT: .... AM / PM		...... Days .... Hours .... Minutes

NAME OF CANDY THAT BEST DESCRIBES THE PEOPLE ON THIS COUCH:

☐ Smarties
☐ Dum-Dums
☐ SweeTARTS
☐ Peeps
☐ Goobers
☐ Hot Tamales
☐ Nerds

ACTIVITIES PERFORMED ON THIS COUCH:

☐ Watching TV   ☐ Chatting   ☐ Chilling out
☐ Playing games   ☐ Sleeping   ☐ Making out
☐ Thinking   ☐ Surfing   ☐ ....

OTHERS IN ATTENDANCE:

....

COUCH THOUGHTS

SEARCH CUSHIONS FOR CHANGE?
☐ Yes, of course   ☐ No, of course not

DID YOU RETURN IT?
☐ Yes, of course   ☐ No, of course not

AMOUNT FOUND: $..............................

OTHER ITEMS FOUND IN CUSHIONS:

....

....

COUCH POTATO SPECTRUM
Shade in the potato to represent where you fall on the couch-potato spectrum.

TOTALLY CHARMING GUEST   TOTAL COUCH POTATO

REPORT CARD	A	B	C	D	F
Ambience					
Comfort					
Cleanliness					
Refreshments					
Roominess					
Conviviality					
OVERALL					

Memorable Moments: _____

_____

_____

_____

_____

_____

Additional Sentiments: _____

_____

_____

_____

_____

_____

Welcome to My Couch

DATE OF VISIT: ....

TIME OF VISIT: .... AM / PM

NAME OF CANDY THAT BEST DESCRIBES THE PEOPLE ON THIS COUCH:

☐ Smarties
☐ Dum-Dums
☐ SweeTARTS
☐ Peeps
☐ Goobers
☐ Hot Tamales
☐ Nerds

COUCH POTATO SPECTRUM

Shade in the potato to represent where you fall on the couch-potato spectrum.

TOTALLY CHARMING GUEST

TOTAL COUCH POTATO

SIGN IN, PLEASE

ACTIVITIES PERFORMED ON THIS COUCH:

☐ Watching TV ☐ Chatting ☐ Chilling out
☐ Playing games ☐ Sleeping ☐ Making out
☐ Thinking ☐ Surfing ☐ ....

OTHERS IN ATTENDANCE:

....

COUCH THOUGHTS

LENGTH OF TIME SPENT ON COUCH:

.... Days .... Hours .... Minutes

SEARCH CUSHIONS FOR CHANGE?

☐ Yes, of course ☐ No, of course not

DID YOU RETURN IT?

☐ Yes, of course ☐ No, of course not

AMOUNT FOUND: $............................

OTHER ITEMS FOUND IN CUSHIONS:

....
....

REPORT CARD	A	B	C	D	F
Ambience					
Comfort					
Cleanliness					
Refreshments					
Roominess					
Conviviality					
OVERALL					

Memorable Moments: _____

_____

_____

_____

_____

_____

Additional Sentiments: _____

_____

_____

_____

_____

_____

Welcome to My Couch

DATE OF VISIT: ....

TIME OF VISIT: .... AM / PM

NAME OF CANDY THAT BEST DESCRIBES THE PEOPLE ON THIS COUCH:

- ☐ Smarties
- ☐ Dum-Dums
- ☐ SweeTARTS
- ☐ Peeps
- ☐ Goobers
- ☐ Hot Tamales
- ☐ Nerds

COUCH POTATO SPECTRUM

Shade in the potato to represent where you fall on the couch-potato spectrum.

TOTALLY CHARMING GUEST   TOTAL COUCH POTATO

SIGN IN, PLEASE

ACTIVITIES PERFORMED ON THIS COUCH:

- ☐ Watching TV
- ☐ Playing games
- ☐ Thinking
- ☐ Chatting
- ☐ Sleeping
- ☐ Surfing
- ☐ Chilling out
- ☐ Making out
- ☐ ....

OTHERS IN ATTENDANCE:

....

COUCH THOUGHTS

LENGTH OF TIME SPENT ON COUCH:

.... Days   .... Hours   .... Minutes

SEARCH CUSHIONS FOR CHANGE?

☐ Yes, of course   ☐ No, of course not

DID YOU RETURN IT?

☐ Yes, of course   ☐ No, of course not

AMOUNT FOUND: $.............................

OTHER ITEMS FOUND IN CUSHIONS:

....

....

REPORT CARD	A	B	C	D	F
Ambience					
Comfort					
Cleanliness					
Refreshments					
Roominess					
Conviviality					
OVERALL					

Memorable Moments: _____

_____

_____

_____

_____

_____

Additional Sentiments: _____

_____

_____

_____

_____

_____

Welcome to My Couch

DATE OF VISIT: ....

TIME OF VISIT: .... AM / PM

SIGN IN, PLEASE

LENGTH OF TIME SPENT ON COUCH:

.... Days .... Hours .... Minutes

NAME OF CANDY THAT BEST DESCRIBES THE PEOPLE ON THIS COUCH:

☐ Smarties
☐ Dum-Dums
☐ SweeTARTS
☐ Peeps
☐ Goobers
☐ Hot Tamales
☐ Nerds

ACTIVITIES PERFORMED ON THIS COUCH:

☐ Watching TV   ☐ Chatting   ☐ Chilling out
☐ Playing games   ☐ Sleeping   ☐ Making out
☐ Thinking   ☐ Surfing   ☐ ....

OTHERS IN ATTENDANCE:

....

COUCH THOUGHTS

SEARCH CUSHIONS FOR CHANGE?
☐ Yes, of course   ☐ No, of course not

DID YOU RETURN IT?
☐ Yes, of course   ☐ No, of course not

AMOUNT FOUND: $.............................

OTHER ITEMS FOUND IN CUSHIONS:

....
....

COUCH POTATO SPECTRUM
Shade in the potato to represent where you fall on the couch-potato spectrum.

TOTALLY
CHARMING
GUEST

TOTAL
COUCH
POTATO

REPORT CARD	A	B	C	D	F
Ambience					
Comfort					
Cleanliness					
Refreshments					
Roominess					
Conviviality					
OVERALL					

Memorable Moments: _____

_____

_____

_____

_____

_____

Additional Sentiments: _____

_____

_____

_____

_____

_____

Welcome to My Couch

DATE OF VISIT: ....

TIME OF VISIT: .... AM / PM

NAME OF CANDY THAT BEST DESCRIBES THE PEOPLE ON THIS COUCH:

- ☐ Smarties
- ☐ Dum-Dums
- ☐ SweeTARTS
- ☐ Peeps
- ☐ Goobers
- ☐ Hot Tamales
- ☐ Nerds

COUCH POTATO SPECTRUM

Shade in the potato to represent where you fall on the couch-potato spectrum.

TOTALLY CHARMING GUEST   TOTAL COUCH POTATO

SIGN IN, PLEASE

ACTIVITIES PERFORMED ON THIS COUCH:

- ☐ Watching TV
- ☐ Playing games
- ☐ Thinking
- ☐ Chatting
- ☐ Sleeping
- ☐ Surfing
- ☐ Chilling out
- ☐ Making out
- ☐ ....

OTHERS IN ATTENDANCE:

....

COUCH THOUGHTS

LENGTH OF TIME SPENT ON COUCH:

...... Days   .... Hours   .... Minutes

SEARCH CUSHIONS FOR CHANGE?

☐ Yes, of course   ☐ No, of course not

DID YOU RETURN IT?

☐ Yes, of course   ☐ No, of course not

AMOUNT FOUND: $............................

OTHER ITEMS FOUND IN CUSHIONS:

....

....

REPORT CARD	A	B	C	D	F
Ambience					
Comfort					
Cleanliness					
Refreshments					
Roominess					
Conviviality					
OVERALL					

Memorable Moments: _____

_____

_____

_____

_____

_____

Additional Sentiments: _____

_____

_____

_____

_____

_____

Welcome to My Couch

DATE OF VISIT: ....

TIME OF VISIT: .... AM / PM

NAME OF CANDY THAT BEST DESCRIBES THE PEOPLE ON THIS COUCH:

☐ Smarties
☐ Dum-Dums
☐ SweeTARTS
☐ Peeps
☐ Goobers
☐ Hot Tamales
☐ Nerds

COUCH POTATO SPECTRUM
Shade in the potato to represent where you fall on the couch-potato spectrum.

TOTALLY CHARMING GUEST

TOTAL COUCH POTATO

SIGN IN, PLEASE

ACTIVITIES PERFORMED ON THIS COUCH:

☐ Watching TV   ☐ Chatting   ☐ Chilling out
☐ Playing games   ☐ Sleeping   ☐ Making out
☐ Thinking   ☐ Surfing   ☐ ....

OTHERS IN ATTENDANCE:

....

COUCH THOUGHTS

LENGTH OF TIME SPENT ON COUCH:

.... Days   .... Hours   .... Minutes

SEARCH CUSHIONS FOR CHANGE?
☐ Yes, of course   ☐ No, of course not

DID YOU RETURN IT?
☐ Yes, of course   ☐ No, of course not

AMOUNT FOUND: $.............................

OTHER ITEMS FOUND IN CUSHIONS:

....
....

REPORT CARD	A	B	C	D	F
Ambience					
Comfort					
Cleanliness					
Refreshments					
Roominess					
Conviviality					
OVERALL					

Memorable Moments: _____
_____
_____
_____
_____
_____

Additional Sentiments: _____
_____
_____
_____
_____
_____

Welcome to My Couch

DATE OF VISIT: ....

TIME OF VISIT: .... AM / PM

NAME OF CANDY THAT BEST DESCRIBES THE PEOPLE ON THIS COUCH:

- ☐ Smarties
- ☐ Dum-Dums
- ☐ SweeTARTS
- ☐ Peeps
- ☐ Goobers
- ☐ Hot Tamales
- ☐ Nerds

COUCH POTATO SPECTRUM

Shade in the potato to represent where you fall on the couch-potato spectrum.

TOTALLY CHARMING GUEST

TOTAL COUCH POTATO

SIGN IN, PLEASE

ACTIVITIES PERFORMED ON THIS COUCH:

- ☐ Watching TV
- ☐ Playing games
- ☐ Thinking
- ☐ Chatting
- ☐ Sleeping
- ☐ Surfing
- ☐ Chilling out
- ☐ Making out
- ☐ ....

OTHERS IN ATTENDANCE:

....

COUCH THOUGHTS

LENGTH OF TIME SPENT ON COUCH:

.... Days   .... Hours   .... Minutes

SEARCH CUSHIONS FOR CHANGE?

☐ Yes, of course   ☐ No, of course not

DID YOU RETURN IT?

☐ Yes, of course   ☐ No, of course not

AMOUNT FOUND: $.............................

OTHER ITEMS FOUND IN CUSHIONS:

....

....

REPORT CARD	A	B	C	D	F
Ambience					
Comfort					
Cleanliness					
Refreshments					
Roominess					
Conviviality					
OVERALL					

Memorable Moments: _____

_____

_____

_____

_____

_____

Additional Sentiments: _____

_____

_____

_____

_____

_____

Welcome to My Couch

DATE OF VISIT: ....

TIME OF VISIT: .... AM / PM

NAME OF CANDY THAT BEST DESCRIBES THE PEOPLE ON THIS COUCH:

- ☐ Smarties
- ☐ Dum-Dums
- ☐ SweeTARTS
- ☐ Peeps
- ☐ Goobers
- ☐ Hot Tamales
- ☐ Nerds

COUCH POTATO SPECTRUM

Shade in the potato to represent where you fall on the couch-potato spectrum.

TOTALLY CHARMING GUEST

TOTAL COUCH POTATO

SIGN IN, PLEASE

ACTIVITIES PERFORMED ON THIS COUCH:

- ☐ Watching TV
- ☐ Playing games
- ☐ Thinking
- ☐ Chatting
- ☐ Sleeping
- ☐ Surfing
- ☐ Chilling out
- ☐ Making out
- ☐ ....

OTHERS IN ATTENDANCE:

....

COUCH THOUGHTS

LENGTH OF TIME SPENT ON COUCH:

...... Days   .... Hours   .... Minutes

SEARCH CUSHIONS FOR CHANGE?

☐ Yes, of course   ☐ No, of course not

DID YOU RETURN IT?

☐ Yes, of course   ☐ No, of course not

AMOUNT FOUND: $............................

OTHER ITEMS FOUND IN CUSHIONS:

....
....

REPORT CARD	A	B	C	D	F
Ambience					
Comfort					
Cleanliness					
Refreshments					
Roominess					
Conviviality					
OVERALL					

Memorable Moments: _____

_____

_____

_____

_____

_____

Additional Sentiments: _____

_____

_____

_____

_____

_____

Welcome to My Couch

DATE OF VISIT: ....

TIME OF VISIT: ....AM / PM

LENGTH OF TIME SPENT ON COUCH:

.... Days   .... Hours   .... Minutes

NAME OF CANDY THAT BEST DESCRIBES THE PEOPLE ON THIS COUCH:

☐ Smarties
☐ Dum-Dums
☐ SweeTARTS
☐ Peeps
☐ Goobers
☐ Hot Tamales
☐ Nerds

ACTIVITIES PERFORMED ON THIS COUCH:

☐ Watching TV   ☐ Chatting   ☐ Chilling out
☐ Playing games   ☐ Sleeping   ☐ Making out
☐ Thinking   ☐ Surfing   ☐ ....

OTHERS IN ATTENDANCE:

....

COUCH THOUGHTS

SEARCH CUSHIONS FOR CHANGE?

☐ Yes, of course   ☐ No, of course not

DID YOU RETURN IT?

☐ Yes, of course   ☐ No, of course not

AMOUNT FOUND: $.............................

OTHER ITEMS FOUND IN CUSHIONS:

....

....

COUCH POTATO SPECTRUM

Shade in the potato to represent where you fall on the couch-potato spectrum.

TOTALLY CHARMING GUEST

TOTAL COUCH POTATO

REPORT CARD	A	B	C	D	F
Ambience					
Comfort					
Cleanliness					
Refreshments					
Roominess					
Conviviality					
OVERALL					

Memorable Moments: _____

_____

_____

_____

_____

_____

Additional Sentiments: _____

_____

_____

_____

_____

Welcome to My Couch

DATE OF VISIT: ....

TIME OF VISIT: .... AM / PM

NAME OF CANDY THAT BEST DESCRIBES THE PEOPLE ON THIS COUCH:

- ☐ Smarties
- ☐ Dum-Dums
- ☐ SweeTARTS
- ☐ Peeps
- ☐ Goobers
- ☐ Hot Tamales
- ☐ Nerds

COUCH POTATO SPECTRUM

Shade in the potato to represent where you fall on the couch-potato spectrum.

TOTALLY CHARMING GUEST — TOTAL COUCH POTATO

SIGN IN, PLEASE

ACTIVITIES PERFORMED ON THIS COUCH:

- ☐ Watching TV
- ☐ Playing games
- ☐ Thinking
- ☐ Chatting
- ☐ Sleeping
- ☐ Surfing
- ☐ Chilling out
- ☐ Making out
- ☐ ....

OTHERS IN ATTENDANCE:

....

COUCH THOUGHTS

LENGTH OF TIME SPENT ON COUCH:

.... Days .... Hours .... Minutes

SEARCH CUSHIONS FOR CHANGE?

☐ Yes, of course ☐ No, of course not

DID YOU RETURN IT?

☐ Yes, of course ☐ No, of course not

AMOUNT FOUND: $............................

OTHER ITEMS FOUND IN CUSHIONS:

....

....

REPORT CARD	A	B	C	D	F
Ambience					
Comfort					
Cleanliness					
Refreshments					
Roominess					
Conviviality					
OVERALL					

Memorable Moments: _____

_____

_____

_____

_____

_____

Additional Sentiments: _____

_____

_____

_____

_____

Welcome to My Couch

DATE OF VISIT: ....

TIME OF VISIT: .... AM / PM

SIGN IN, PLEASE

LENGTH OF TIME SPENT ON COUCH:

.... Days .... Hours .... Minutes

NAME OF CANDY THAT BEST DESCRIBES THE PEOPLE ON THIS COUCH:

- ☐ Smarties
- ☐ Dum-Dums
- ☐ SweeTARTS
- ☐ Peeps
- ☐ Goobers
- ☐ Hot Tamales
- ☐ Nerds

ACTIVITIES PERFORMED ON THIS COUCH:

- ☐ Watching TV
- ☐ Playing games
- ☐ Thinking
- ☐ Chatting
- ☐ Sleeping
- ☐ Surfing
- ☐ Chilling out
- ☐ Making out
- ☐ ....

OTHERS IN ATTENDANCE:

....

COUCH THOUGHTS

SEARCH CUSHIONS FOR CHANGE?

☐ Yes, of course   ☐ No, of course not

DID YOU RETURN IT?

☐ Yes, of course   ☐ No, of course not

AMOUNT FOUND: $.............................

OTHER ITEMS FOUND IN CUSHIONS:

....

....

COUCH POTATO SPECTRUM

Shade in the potato to represent where you fall on the couch-potato spectrum.

TOTALLY CHARMING GUEST

TOTAL COUCH POTATO

REPORT CARD	A	B	C	D	F
Ambience					
Comfort					
Cleanliness					
Refreshments					
Roominess					
Conviviality					
OVERALL					

Memorable Moments: _____

_____

_____

_____

_____

_____

Additional Sentiments: _____

_____

_____

_____

_____

_____

Welcome to My Couch

DATE OF VISIT: ....

TIME OF VISIT: .... AM / PM

NAME OF CANDY THAT BEST DESCRIBES THE PEOPLE ON THIS COUCH:

- ☐ Smarties
- ☐ Dum-Dums
- ☐ SweeTARTS
- ☐ Peeps
- ☐ Goobers
- ☐ Hot Tamales
- ☐ Nerds

COUCH POTATO SPECTRUM

Shade in the potato to represent where you fall on the couch-potato spectrum.

TOTALLY CHARMING GUEST

TOTAL COUCH POTATO

SIGN IN, PLEASE

ACTIVITIES PERFORMED ON THIS COUCH:

- ☐ Watching TV
- ☐ Chatting
- ☐ Chilling out
- ☐ Playing games
- ☐ Sleeping
- ☐ Making out
- ☐ Thinking
- ☐ Surfing
- ☐ ....

OTHERS IN ATTENDANCE:

....

COUCH THOUGHTS

LENGTH OF TIME SPENT ON COUCH:

.... Days   .... Hours   .... Minutes

SEARCH CUSHIONS FOR CHANGE?

☐ Yes, of course   ☐ No, of course not

DID YOU RETURN IT?

☐ Yes, of course   ☐ No, of course not

AMOUNT FOUND: $.............................

OTHER ITEMS FOUND IN CUSHIONS:

....

....

REPORT CARD	A	B	C	D	F
Ambience					
Comfort					
Cleanliness					
Refreshments					
Roominess					
Conviviality					
OVERALL					

Memorable Moments: _____

_____

_____

_____

_____

_____

Additional Sentiments: _____

_____

_____

_____

_____

_____

Welcome to My Couch

DATE OF VISIT: ....

TIME OF VISIT: .... AM / PM

NAME OF CANDY THAT BEST DESCRIBES THE PEOPLE ON THIS COUCH:

- ☐ Smarties
- ☐ Dum-Dums
- ☐ SweeTARTS
- ☐ Peeps
- ☐ Goobers
- ☐ Hot Tamales
- ☐ Nerds

COUCH POTATO SPECTRUM

Shade in the potato to represent where you fall on the couch-potato spectrum.

TOTALLY
CHARMING
GUEST

TOTAL
COUCH
POTATO

SIGN IN, PLEASE

ACTIVITIES PERFORMED ON THIS COUCH:

- ☐ Watching TV
- ☐ Playing games
- ☐ Thinking
- ☐ Chatting
- ☐ Sleeping
- ☐ Surfing
- ☐ Chilling out
- ☐ Making out
- ☐ ....

OTHERS IN ATTENDANCE:

....

COUCH THOUGHTS

LENGTH OF TIME SPENT ON COUCH:

.... Days   .... Hours   .... Minutes

SEARCH CUSHIONS FOR CHANGE?

☐ Yes, of course   ☐ No, of course not

DID YOU RETURN IT?

☐ Yes, of course   ☐ No, of course not

AMOUNT FOUND: $.............................

OTHER ITEMS FOUND IN CUSHIONS:

....

....

REPORT CARD	A	B	C	D	F
Ambience					
Comfort					
Cleanliness					
Refreshments					
Roominess					
Conviviality					
OVERALL					

Memorable Moments: _____

_____

_____

_____

_____

_____

Additional Sentiments: _____

_____

_____

_____

_____

_____

Welcome to My Couch

DATE OF VISIT: ....

TIME OF VISIT: .... AM / PM

NAME OF CANDY THAT BEST DESCRIBES THE PEOPLE ON THIS COUCH:

- ☐ Smarties
- ☐ Dum-Dums
- ☐ SweeTARTS
- ☐ Peeps
- ☐ Goobers
- ☐ Hot Tamales
- ☐ Nerds

COUCH POTATO SPECTRUM

Shade in the potato to represent where you fall on the couch-potato spectrum.

TOTALLY CHARMING GUEST   TOTAL COUCH POTATO

SIGN IN, PLEASE

ACTIVITIES PERFORMED ON THIS COUCH:

- ☐ Watching TV
- ☐ Playing games
- ☐ Thinking
- ☐ Chatting
- ☐ Sleeping
- ☐ Surfing
- ☐ Chilling out
- ☐ Making out
- ☐ ....

OTHERS IN ATTENDANCE:

....

COUCH THOUGHTS

LENGTH OF TIME SPENT ON COUCH:

.... Days .... Hours .... Minutes

SEARCH CUSHIONS FOR CHANGE?

☐ Yes, of course   ☐ No, of course not

DID YOU RETURN IT?

☐ Yes, of course   ☐ No, of course not

AMOUNT FOUND: $.............................

OTHER ITEMS FOUND IN CUSHIONS:

....

....

REPORT CARD	A	B	C	D	F
Ambience					
Comfort					
Cleanliness					
Refreshments					
Roominess					
Conviviality					
OVERALL					

Memorable Moments: _____

_____

_____

_____

_____

_____

Additional Sentiments: _____

_____

_____

_____

_____

_____

Welcome to My Couch

DATE OF VISIT: ....

TIME OF VISIT: .... AM / PM

SIGN IN, PLEASE

LENGTH OF TIME SPENT ON COUCH:
.... Days   .... Hours   .... Minutes

NAME OF CANDY THAT BEST DESCRIBES THE PEOPLE ON THIS COUCH:

- ☐ Smarties
- ☐ Dum-Dums
- ☐ SweeTARTS
- ☐ Peeps
- ☐ Goobers
- ☐ Hot Tamales
- ☐ Nerds

ACTIVITIES PERFORMED ON THIS COUCH:

- ☐ Watching TV
- ☐ Playing games
- ☐ Thinking
- ☐ Chatting
- ☐ Sleeping
- ☐ Surfing
- ☐ Chilling out
- ☐ Making out
- ☐ ....

OTHERS IN ATTENDANCE:
....

COUCH THOUGHTS

SEARCH CUSHIONS FOR CHANGE?
☐ Yes, of course   ☐ No, of course not

DID YOU RETURN IT?
☐ Yes, of course   ☐ No, of course not

AMOUNT FOUND: $........................

OTHER ITEMS FOUND IN CUSHIONS:
....
....

COUCH POTATO SPECTRUM
Shade in the potato to represent where you fall on the couch-potato spectrum.

TOTALLY CHARMING GUEST

TOTAL COUCH POTATO

REPORT CARD	A	B	C	D	F
Ambience					
Comfort					
Cleanliness					
Refreshments					
Roominess					
Conviviality					
OVERALL					

Memorable Moments: _____

_____

_____

_____

_____

_____

Additional Sentiments: _____

_____

_____

_____

_____

_____

Welcome to My Couch

DATE OF VISIT: ....

TIME OF VISIT: .... AM / PM

NAME OF CANDY THAT BEST DESCRIBES THE PEOPLE ON THIS COUCH:

- ☐ Smarties
- ☐ Dum-Dums
- ☐ SweeTARTS
- ☐ Peeps
- ☐ Goobers
- ☐ Hot Tamales
- ☐ Nerds

COUCH POTATO SPECTRUM

Shade in the potato to represent where you fall on the couch-potato spectrum.

TOTALLY CHARMING GUEST

TOTAL COUCH POTATO

SIGN IN, PLEASE

ACTIVITIES PERFORMED ON THIS COUCH:

- ☐ Watching TV
- ☐ Playing games
- ☐ Thinking
- ☐ Chatting
- ☐ Sleeping
- ☐ Surfing
- ☐ Chilling out
- ☐ Making out
- ☐ ....

OTHERS IN ATTENDANCE:

....

COUCH THOUGHTS

LENGTH OF TIME SPENT ON COUCH:

...... Days .... Hours .... Minutes

SEARCH CUSHIONS FOR CHANGE?

☐ Yes, of course   ☐ No, of course not

DID YOU RETURN IT?

☐ Yes, of course   ☐ No, of course not

AMOUNT FOUND: $...........................

OTHER ITEMS FOUND IN CUSHIONS:

....

....

REPORT CARD	A	B	C	D	F
Ambience					
Comfort					
Cleanliness					
Refreshments					
Roominess					
Conviviality					
OVERALL					

Memorable Moments: _____
_____
_____
_____
_____
_____

Additional Sentiments: _____
_____
_____
_____
_____

Welcome to My Couch

DATE OF VISIT: ....

TIME OF VISIT: .... AM / PM

SIGN IN, PLEASE

LENGTH OF TIME SPENT ON COUCH:

...... Days .... Hours .... Minutes

NAME OF CANDY THAT BEST DESCRIBES THE PEOPLE ON THIS COUCH:

- ☐ Smarties
- ☐ Dum-Dums
- ☐ SweeTARTS
- ☐ Peeps
- ☐ Goobers
- ☐ Hot Tamales
- ☐ Nerds

ACTIVITIES PERFORMED ON THIS COUCH:

- ☐ Watching TV
- ☐ Playing games
- ☐ Thinking
- ☐ Chatting
- ☐ Sleeping
- ☐ Surfing
- ☐ Chilling out
- ☐ Making out
- ☐ ....

OTHERS IN ATTENDANCE:

....

COUCH THOUGHTS

SEARCH CUSHIONS FOR CHANGE?

☐ Yes, of course ☐ No, of course not

DID YOU RETURN IT?

☐ Yes, of course ☐ No, of course not

AMOUNT FOUND: $..........................

OTHER ITEMS FOUND IN CUSHIONS:

....

....

....

COUCH POTATO SPECTRUM

Shade in the potato to represent where you fall on the couch-potato spectrum.

TOTALLY CHARMING GUEST

TOTAL COUCH POTATO

REPORT CARD	A	B	C	D	F
Ambience					
Comfort					
Cleanliness					
Refreshments					
Roominess					
Conviviality					
OVERALL					

Memorable Moments: _____

_____

_____

_____

_____

_____

Additional Sentiments: _____

_____

_____

_____

_____

_____

Welcome to My Couch

DATE OF VISIT: ....

TIME OF VISIT: .... AM / PM

NAME OF CANDY THAT BEST DESCRIBES THE PEOPLE ON THIS COUCH:

- ☐ Smarties
- ☐ Dum-Dums
- ☐ SweeTARTS
- ☐ Peeps
- ☐ Goobers
- ☐ Hot Tamales
- ☐ Nerds

COUCH POTATO SPECTRUM

Shade in the potato to represent where you fall on the couch-potato spectrum.

TOTALLY CHARMING GUEST   TOTAL COUCH POTATO

SIGN IN, PLEASE

ACTIVITIES PERFORMED ON THIS COUCH:

- ☐ Watching TV
- ☐ Playing games
- ☐ Thinking
- ☐ Chatting
- ☐ Sleeping
- ☐ Surfing
- ☐ Chilling out
- ☐ Making out
- ☐ ....

OTHERS IN ATTENDANCE:

....

COUCH THOUGHTS

LENGTH OF TIME SPENT ON COUCH:

.... Days   .... Hours   .... Minutes

SEARCH CUSHIONS FOR CHANGE?

☐ Yes, of course   ☐ No, of course not

DID YOU RETURN IT?

☐ Yes, of course   ☐ No, of course not

AMOUNT FOUND: $............................

OTHER ITEMS FOUND IN CUSHIONS:

....

....

REPORT CARD	A	B	C	D	F
Ambience					
Comfort					
Cleanliness					
Refreshments					
Roominess					
Conviviality					
OVERALL					

Memorable Moments: _____

_____

_____

_____

_____

_____

Additional Sentiments: _____

_____

_____

_____

_____

_____

Welcome to My Couch

DATE OF VISIT: ....

TIME OF VISIT: .... AM / PM

SIGN IN, PLEASE

LENGTH OF TIME SPENT ON COUCH:

...... Days .... Hours .... Minutes

NAME OF CANDY THAT BEST DESCRIBES THE PEOPLE ON THIS COUCH:

- ☐ Smarties
- ☐ Dum-Dums
- ☐ SweeTARTS
- ☐ Peeps
- ☐ Goobers
- ☐ Hot Tamales
- ☐ Nerds

ACTIVITIES PERFORMED ON THIS COUCH:

- ☐ Watching TV
- ☐ Playing games
- ☐ Thinking
- ☐ Chatting
- ☐ Sleeping
- ☐ Surfing
- ☐ Chilling out
- ☐ Making out
- ☐ ....

OTHERS IN ATTENDANCE:

....

COUCH THOUGHTS

SEARCH CUSHIONS FOR CHANGE?

☐ Yes, of course ☐ No, of course not

DID YOU RETURN IT?

☐ Yes, of course ☐ No, of course not

AMOUNT FOUND: $............................

OTHER ITEMS FOUND IN CUSHIONS:

....
....

COUCH POTATO SPECTRUM

Shade in the potato to represent where you fall on the couch-potato spectrum.

TOTALLY CHARMING GUEST

TOTAL COUCH POTATO

REPORT CARD	A	B	C	D	F
Ambience					
Comfort					
Cleanliness					
Refreshments					
Roominess					
Conviviality					
OVERALL					

Memorable Moments: _____

_____

_____

_____

_____

_____

Additional Sentiments: _____

_____

_____

_____

_____

_____

Welcome to My Couch

DATE OF VISIT: ....

TIME OF VISIT: .... AM / PM

NAME OF CANDY THAT BEST DESCRIBES THE PEOPLE ON THIS COUCH:

- ☐ Smarties
- ☐ Dum-Dums
- ☐ SweeTARTS
- ☐ Peeps
- ☐ Goobers
- ☐ Hot Tamales
- ☐ Nerds

COUCH POTATO SPECTRUM

Shade in the potato to represent where you fall on the couch-potato spectrum.

TOTALLY CHARMING GUEST   TOTAL COUCH POTATO

SIGN IN, PLEASE

ACTIVITIES PERFORMED ON THIS COUCH:

- ☐ Watching TV
- ☐ Playing games
- ☐ Thinking
- ☐ Chatting
- ☐ Sleeping
- ☐ Surfing
- ☐ Chilling out
- ☐ Making out
- ☐ ....

OTHERS IN ATTENDANCE:

....

COUCH THOUGHTS

LENGTH OF TIME SPENT ON COUCH:

...... Days .... Hours .... Minutes

SEARCH CUSHIONS FOR CHANGE?

☐ Yes, of course ☐ No, of course not

DID YOU RETURN IT?

☐ Yes, of course ☐ No, of course not

AMOUNT FOUND: $.............................

OTHER ITEMS FOUND IN CUSHIONS:

....

....

REPORT CARD	A	B	C	D	F
Ambience					
Comfort					
Cleanliness					
Refreshments					
Roominess					
Conviviality					
OVERALL					

Memorable Moments: _____
_____
_____
_____
_____

Additional Sentiments: _____
_____
_____
_____
_____

Welcome to My Couch

DATE OF VISIT: ....

TIME OF VISIT: .... AM / PM

SIGN IN, PLEASE

LENGTH OF TIME SPENT ON COUCH:

.... Days   .... Hours   .... Minutes

NAME OF CANDY THAT BEST DESCRIBES THE PEOPLE ON THIS COUCH:

- ☐ Smarties
- ☐ Dum-Dums
- ☐ SweeTARTS
- ☐ Peeps
- ☐ Goobers
- ☐ Hot Tamales
- ☐ Nerds

ACTIVITIES PERFORMED ON THIS COUCH:

- ☐ Watching TV
- ☐ Playing games
- ☐ Thinking
- ☐ Chatting
- ☐ Sleeping
- ☐ Surfing
- ☐ Chilling out
- ☐ Making out
- ☐ ....

OTHERS IN ATTENDANCE:

....

COUCH THOUGHTS

SEARCH CUSHIONS FOR CHANGE?

☐ Yes, of course   ☐ No, of course not

DID YOU RETURN IT?

☐ Yes, of course   ☐ No, of course not

AMOUNT FOUND: $.............................

OTHER ITEMS FOUND IN CUSHIONS:

....

....

....

COUCH POTATO SPECTRUM

Shade in the potato to represent where you fall on the couch-potato spectrum.

TOTALLY CHARMING GUEST   TOTAL COUCH POTATO

REPORT CARD	A	B	C	D	F
Ambience					
Comfort					
Cleanliness					
Refreshments					
Roominess					
Conviviality					
OVERALL					

Memorable Moments: _____

_____

_____

_____

_____

_____

Additional Sentiments: _____

_____

_____

_____

_____

_____

Welcome to My Couch

DATE OF VISIT: ....

TIME OF VISIT: .... AM / PM

NAME OF CANDY THAT BEST DESCRIBES THE PEOPLE ON THIS COUCH:

- ☐ Smarties
- ☐ Dum-Dums
- ☐ SweeTARTS
- ☐ Peeps
- ☐ Goobers
- ☐ Hot Tamales
- ☐ Nerds

COUCH POTATO SPECTRUM

Shade in the potato to represent where you fall on the couch-potato spectrum.

TOTALLY CHARMING GUEST   TOTAL COUCH POTATO

SIGN IN, PLEASE

ACTIVITIES PERFORMED ON THIS COUCH:

- ☐ Watching TV
- ☐ Playing games
- ☐ Thinking
- ☐ Chatting
- ☐ Sleeping
- ☐ Surfing
- ☐ Chilling out
- ☐ Making out
- ☐ ....

OTHERS IN ATTENDANCE:

....

COUCH THOUGHTS

LENGTH OF TIME SPENT ON COUCH:

.... Days   .... Hours   .... Minutes

SEARCH CUSHIONS FOR CHANGE?

☐ Yes, of course   ☐ No, of course not

DID YOU RETURN IT?

☐ Yes, of course   ☐ No, of course not

AMOUNT FOUND: $...........................

OTHER ITEMS FOUND IN CUSHIONS:

....

....

REPORT CARD	A	B	C	D	F
Ambience					
Comfort					
Cleanliness					
Refreshments					
Roominess					
Conviviality					
OVERALL					

Memorable Moments: _____

_____

_____

_____

_____

_____

Additional Sentiments: _____

_____

_____

_____

_____

_____

Welcome to My Couch

DATE OF VISIT: ....

TIME OF VISIT: .... AM / PM

NAME OF CANDY THAT BEST DESCRIBES THE PEOPLE ON THIS COUCH:

- ☐ Smarties
- ☐ Dum-Dums
- ☐ SweeTARTS
- ☐ Peeps
- ☐ Goobers
- ☐ Hot Tamales
- ☐ Nerds

COUCH POTATO SPECTRUM

Shade in the potato to represent where you fall on the couch-potato spectrum.

TOTALLY CHARMING GUEST   TOTAL COUCH POTATO

SIGN IN, PLEASE

ACTIVITIES PERFORMED ON THIS COUCH:

- ☐ Watching TV
- ☐ Playing games
- ☐ Thinking
- ☐ Chatting
- ☐ Sleeping
- ☐ Surfing
- ☐ Chilling out
- ☐ Making out
- ☐ ....

OTHERS IN ATTENDANCE:

....

COUCH THOUGHTS

LENGTH OF TIME SPENT ON COUCH:

...... Days   ...... Hours   ...... Minutes

SEARCH CUSHIONS FOR CHANGE?

☐ Yes, of course   ☐ No, of course not

DID YOU RETURN IT?

☐ Yes, of course   ☐ No, of course not

AMOUNT FOUND: $...........................

OTHER ITEMS FOUND IN CUSHIONS:

....

....

REPORT CARD	A	B	C	D	F
Ambience					
Comfort					
Cleanliness					
Refreshments					
Roominess					
Conviviality					
OVERALL					

Memorable Moments: _____

_____
_____
_____
_____
_____

Additional Sentiments: _____

_____
_____
_____
_____
_____

Welcome to My Couch

DATE OF VISIT: ....

TIME OF VISIT: .... AM / PM

NAME OF CANDY THAT BEST DESCRIBES THE PEOPLE ON THIS COUCH:

- ☐ Smarties
- ☐ Dum-Dums
- ☐ SweeTARTS
- ☐ Peeps
- ☐ Goobers
- ☐ Hot Tamales
- ☐ Nerds

COUCH POTATO SPECTRUM

Shade in the potato to represent where you fall on the couch-potato spectrum.

TOTALLY CHARMING GUEST

TOTAL COUCH POTATO

SIGN IN, PLEASE

ACTIVITIES PERFORMED ON THIS COUCH:

- ☐ Watching TV
- ☐ Playing games
- ☐ Thinking
- ☐ Chatting
- ☐ Sleeping
- ☐ Surfing
- ☐ Chilling out
- ☐ Making out
- ☐ ....

OTHERS IN ATTENDANCE:

....

COUCH THOUGHTS

LENGTH OF TIME SPENT ON COUCH:

...... Days .... Hours .... Minutes

SEARCH CUSHIONS FOR CHANGE?

☐ Yes, of course ☐ No, of course not

DID YOU RETURN IT?

☐ Yes, of course ☐ No, of course not

AMOUNT FOUND: $............................

OTHER ITEMS FOUND IN CUSHIONS:

....

....

....

REPORT CARD	A	B	C	D	F
Ambience					
Comfort					
Cleanliness					
Refreshments					
Roominess					
Conviviality					
OVERALL					

Memorable Moments: _____

_____

_____

_____

_____

_____

Additional Sentiments: _____

_____

_____

_____

_____

_____

Welcome to My Couch

DATE OF VISIT: ....

TIME OF VISIT: .... AM / PM

NAME OF CANDY THAT BEST DESCRIBES THE PEOPLE ON THIS COUCH:

- ☐ Smarties
- ☐ Dum-Dums
- ☐ SweeTARTS
- ☐ Peeps
- ☐ Goobers
- ☐ Hot Tamales
- ☐ Nerds

COUCH POTATO SPECTRUM

Shade in the potato to represent where you fall on the couch-potato spectrum.

TOTALLY CHARMING GUEST — TOTAL COUCH POTATO

SIGN IN, PLEASE

ACTIVITIES PERFORMED ON THIS COUCH:

- ☐ Watching TV
- ☐ Playing games
- ☐ Thinking
- ☐ Chatting
- ☐ Sleeping
- ☐ Surfing
- ☐ Chilling out
- ☐ Making out
- ☐ ....

OTHERS IN ATTENDANCE:

....

COUCH THOUGHTS

LENGTH OF TIME SPENT ON COUCH:

.... Days .... Hours .... Minutes

SEARCH CUSHIONS FOR CHANGE?

☐ Yes, of course ☐ No, of course not

DID YOU RETURN IT?

☐ Yes, of course ☐ No, of course not

AMOUNT FOUND: $............................

OTHER ITEMS FOUND IN CUSHIONS:

....

....

REPORT CARD	A	B	C	D	F
Ambience					
Comfort					
Cleanliness					
Refreshments					
Roominess					
Conviviality					
OVERALL					

Memorable Moments: _____

_____

_____

_____

_____

Additional Sentiments: _____

_____

_____

_____

_____

Welcome to My Couch

DATE OF VISIT: ....

TIME OF VISIT: .... AM / PM

NAME OF CANDY THAT BEST DESCRIBES THE PEOPLE ON THIS COUCH:

- ☐ Smarties
- ☐ Dum-Dums
- ☐ SweeTARTS
- ☐ Peeps
- ☐ Goobers
- ☐ Hot Tamales
- ☐ Nerds

COUCH POTATO SPECTRUM
Shade in the potato to represent where you fall on the couch-potato spectrum.

TOTALLY CHARMING GUEST   TOTAL COUCH POTATO

SIGN IN, PLEASE

ACTIVITIES PERFORMED ON THIS COUCH:

- ☐ Watching TV
- ☐ Playing games
- ☐ Thinking
- ☐ Chatting
- ☐ Sleeping
- ☐ Surfing
- ☐ Chilling out
- ☐ Making out
- ☐ ....

OTHERS IN ATTENDANCE:

....

COUCH THOUGHTS

LENGTH OF TIME SPENT ON COUCH:

.... Days   .... Hours   .... Minutes

SEARCH CUSHIONS FOR CHANGE?

☐ Yes, of course   ☐ No, of course not

DID YOU RETURN IT?

☐ Yes, of course   ☐ No, of course not

AMOUNT FOUND: $..............................

OTHER ITEMS FOUND IN CUSHIONS:

....

....

REPORT CARD	A	B	C	D	F
Ambience					
Comfort					
Cleanliness					
Refreshments					
Roominess					
Conviviality					
OVERALL					

Memorable Moments: _____
_____
_____
_____
_____
_____

Additional Sentiments: _____
_____
_____
_____
_____
_____

Welcome to My Couch

DATE OF VISIT: ....

TIME OF VISIT: .... AM / PM

NAME OF CANDY THAT BEST DESCRIBES THE PEOPLE ON THIS COUCH:

- ☐ Smarties
- ☐ Dum-Dums
- ☐ SweeTARTS
- ☐ Peeps
- ☐ Goobers
- ☐ Hot Tamales
- ☐ Nerds

COUCH POTATO SPECTRUM

Shade in the potato to represent where you fall on the couch-potato spectrum.

TOTALLY CHARMING GUEST

TOTAL COUCH POTATO

SIGN IN, PLEASE

ACTIVITIES PERFORMED ON THIS COUCH:

- ☐ Watching TV
- ☐ Playing games
- ☐ Thinking
- ☐ Chatting
- ☐ Sleeping
- ☐ Surfing
- ☐ Chilling out
- ☐ Making out
- ☐ ....

OTHERS IN ATTENDANCE:

....

COUCH THOUGHTS

LENGTH OF TIME SPENT ON COUCH:

...... Days .... Hours .... Minutes

SEARCH CUSHIONS FOR CHANGE?

☐ Yes, of course   ☐ No, of course not

DID YOU RETURN IT?

☐ Yes, of course   ☐ No, of course not

AMOUNT FOUND: $.............................

OTHER ITEMS FOUND IN CUSHIONS:

....

....

REPORT CARD	A	B	C	D	F
Ambience					
Comfort					
Cleanliness					
Refreshments					
Roominess					
Conviviality					
OVERALL					

Memorable Moments: _____

_____

_____

_____

_____

Additional Sentiments: _____

_____

_____

_____

_____

Welcome to My Couch

DATE OF VISIT: ....

TIME OF VISIT: .... AM / PM

NAME OF CANDY THAT BEST DESCRIBES THE PEOPLE ON THIS COUCH:

- ☐ Smarties
- ☐ Dum-Dums
- ☐ SweeTARTS
- ☐ Peeps
- ☐ Goobers
- ☐ Hot Tamales
- ☐ Nerds

COUCH POTATO SPECTRUM

Shade in the potato to represent where you fall on the couch-potato spectrum.

TOTALLY CHARMING GUEST   **TOTAL COUCH POTATO**

SIGN IN, PLEASE

ACTIVITIES PERFORMED ON THIS COUCH:

- ☐ Watching TV
- ☐ Playing games
- ☐ Thinking
- ☐ Chatting
- ☐ Sleeping
- ☐ Surfing
- ☐ Chilling out
- ☐ Making out
- ☐ ....

OTHERS IN ATTENDANCE:

....

COUCH THOUGHTS

LENGTH OF TIME SPENT ON COUCH:

...... Days .... Hours .... Minutes

SEARCH CUSHIONS FOR CHANGE?

☐ Yes, of course   ☐ No, of course not

DID YOU RETURN IT?

☐ Yes, of course   ☐ No, of course not

AMOUNT FOUND: $..............................

OTHER ITEMS FOUND IN CUSHIONS:

....

....

REPORT CARD	A	B	C	D	F
Ambience					
Comfort					
Cleanliness					
Refreshments					
Roominess					
Conviviality					
OVERALL					

Memorable Moments: _____

_____

_____

_____

_____

_____

Additional Sentiments: _____

_____

_____

_____

_____

_____

Welcome to My Couch

DATE OF VISIT: ....

TIME OF VISIT: .... AM / PM

NAME OF CANDY THAT BEST DESCRIBES THE PEOPLE ON THIS COUCH:

- ☐ Smarties
- ☐ Dum-Dums
- ☐ SweeTARTS
- ☐ Peeps
- ☐ Goobers
- ☐ Hot Tamales
- ☐ Nerds

COUCH POTATO SPECTRUM

Shade in the potato to represent where you fall on the couch-potato spectrum.

TOTALLY CHARMING GUEST — TOTAL COUCH POTATO

SIGN IN, PLEASE

ACTIVITIES PERFORMED ON THIS COUCH:

- ☐ Watching TV
- ☐ Playing games
- ☐ Thinking
- ☐ Chatting
- ☐ Sleeping
- ☐ Surfing
- ☐ Chilling out
- ☐ Making out
- ☐ ....

OTHERS IN ATTENDANCE:

....

COUCH THOUGHTS

LENGTH OF TIME SPENT ON COUCH:

.... Days   .... Hours   .... Minutes

SEARCH CUSHIONS FOR CHANGE?

☐ Yes, of course   ☐ No, of course not

DID YOU RETURN IT?

☐ Yes, of course   ☐ No, of course not

AMOUNT FOUND: $............................

OTHER ITEMS FOUND IN CUSHIONS:

....

....

REPORT CARD	A	B	C	D	F
Ambience					
Comfort					
Cleanliness					
Refreshments					
Roominess					
Conviviality					
OVERALL					

Memorable Moments: _____
_____
_____
_____
_____
_____

Additional Sentiments: _____
_____
_____
_____
_____
_____

Welcome to My Couch

DATE OF VISIT: ....

TIME OF VISIT: .... AM / PM

NAME OF CANDY THAT BEST DESCRIBES THE PEOPLE ON THIS COUCH:

- ☐ Smarties
- ☐ Dum-Dums
- ☐ SweeTARTS
- ☐ Peeps
- ☐ Goobers
- ☐ Hot Tamales
- ☐ Nerds

COUCH POTATO SPECTRUM

Shade in the potato to represent where you fall on the couch-potato spectrum.

TOTALLY
CHARMING
GUEST

TOTAL
COUCH
POTATO

SIGN IN, PLEASE

ACTIVITIES PERFORMED ON THIS COUCH:

- ☐ Watching TV
- ☐ Playing games
- ☐ Thinking
- ☐ Chatting
- ☐ Sleeping
- ☐ Surfing
- ☐ Chilling out
- ☐ Making out
- ☐ ....

OTHERS IN ATTENDANCE:

....

COUCH THOUGHTS

LENGTH OF TIME SPENT ON COUCH:

.... Days   .... Hours   .... Minutes

SEARCH CUSHIONS FOR CHANGE?

☐ Yes, of course   ☐ No, of course not

DID YOU RETURN IT?

☐ Yes, of course   ☐ No, of course not

AMOUNT FOUND: $..........................

OTHER ITEMS FOUND IN CUSHIONS:

....

....

REPORT CARD	A	B	C	D	F
Ambience					
Comfort					
Cleanliness					
Refreshments					
Roominess					
Conviviality					
OVERALL					

Memorable Moments: _____

_____

_____

_____

_____

Additional Sentiments: _____

_____

_____

_____

_____

Welcome to My Couch

DATE OF VISIT: ....

TIME OF VISIT: .... AM / PM

NAME OF CANDY THAT BEST DESCRIBES THE PEOPLE ON THIS COUCH:

☐ Smarties
☐ Dum-Dums
☐ SweeTARTS
☐ Peeps
☐ Goobers
☐ Hot Tamales
☐ Nerds

COUCH POTATO SPECTRUM
Shade in the potato to represent where you fall on the couch-potato spectrum.

TOTALLY CHARMING GUEST

TOTAL COUCH POTATO

SIGN IN, PLEASE

ACTIVITIES PERFORMED ON THIS COUCH:

☐ Watching TV   ☐ Chatting   ☐ Chilling out
☐ Playing games   ☐ Sleeping   ☐ Making out
☐ Thinking   ☐ Surfing   ☐ ....

OTHERS IN ATTENDANCE:

....

COUCH THOUGHTS

LENGTH OF TIME SPENT ON COUCH:

.... Days   .... Hours   .... Minutes

SEARCH CUSHIONS FOR CHANGE?
☐ Yes, of course   ☐ No, of course not

DID YOU RETURN IT?
☐ Yes, of course   ☐ No, of course not

AMOUNT FOUND: $..............................

OTHER ITEMS FOUND IN CUSHIONS:

....

....

REPORT CARD	A	B	C	D	F
Ambience					
Comfort					
Cleanliness					
Refreshments					
Roominess					
Conviviality					
OVERALL					

Memorable Moments: _____
_____
_____
_____
_____
_____

Additional Sentiments: _____
_____
_____
_____
_____
_____

Welcome to My Couch

DATE OF VISIT: ....

TIME OF VISIT: .... AM / PM

NAME OF CANDY THAT BEST DESCRIBES THE PEOPLE ON THIS COUCH:

☐ Smarties
☐ Dum-Dums
☐ SweeTARTS
☐ Peeps
☐ Goobers
☐ Hot Tamales
☐ Nerds

COUCH POTATO SPECTRUM
Shade in the potato to represent where you fall on the couch-potato spectrum.

TOTALLY
CHARMING
GUEST

TOTAL
COUCH
POTATO

SIGN IN, PLEASE

ACTIVITIES PERFORMED ON THIS COUCH:

☐ Watching TV   ☐ Chatting   ☐ Chilling out
☐ Playing games   ☐ Sleeping   ☐ Making out
☐ Thinking   ☐ Surfing   ☐ ....

OTHERS IN ATTENDANCE:
....

COUCH THOUGHTS

LENGTH OF TIME SPENT ON COUCH:
.... Days   .... Hours   .... Minutes

SEARCH CUSHIONS FOR CHANGE?
☐ Yes, of course   ☐ No, of course not

DID YOU RETURN IT?
☐ Yes, of course   ☐ No, of course not

AMOUNT FOUND: $.............................

OTHER ITEMS FOUND IN CUSHIONS:
....
....

REPORT CARD	A	B	C	D	F
Ambience					
Comfort					
Cleanliness					
Refreshments					
Roominess					
Conviviality					
OVERALL					